Guest Spot
Duets

C000152745

GREATEST HITS

Playalong Duets *for* Alto Saxophone

Exclusive Distributors:
Music Sales Limited
8/9 Frith Street, London W1D 3JB, England.
Music Sales Pty Limited
120 Rothschild Avenue, Rosebery, NSW 2018, Australia.

Order No. AM970948
ISBN 0-7119-8918-4
This book © Copyright 2001 by Wise Publications.

Music arranged by Jack Long.
Music processed by Enigma Music Production Services.
Cover photography by George Taylor.
Printed and bound in Malta by Interprint Limited.

CD backing tracks arranged by Paul Honey and John Moores.
Instrumental solos by John Whelan.
Engineered by Kester Sims.

Your Guarantee of Quality:
As publishers, we strive to produce every book to
the highest commercial standards.
The music has been freshly engraved and the book has been
carefully designed to minimise awkward page turns and
to make playing from it a real pleasure.
Particular care has been given to specifying acid-free, neutral-sized
paper made from pulps which have not been elemental chlorine bleached.
This pulp is from farmed sustainable forests and was
produced with special regard for the environment.
Throughout, the printing and binding have been planned to
ensure a sturdy, attractive publication which should give years of enjoyment.
If your copy fails to meet our high standards,
please inform us and we will gladly replace it.

Music Sales' complete catalogue describes thousands of
titles and is available in full colour sections by subject,
direct from Music Sales Limited.
Please state your areas of interest and send a
cheque/postal order for £1.50 for postage to:
Music Sales Limited, Newmarket Road, Bury St. Edmunds, Suffolk IP33 3YB.

www.musicsales.com

WISE PUBLICATIONS
London/New York/Paris/Sydney/Copenhagen/Madrid/Tokyo

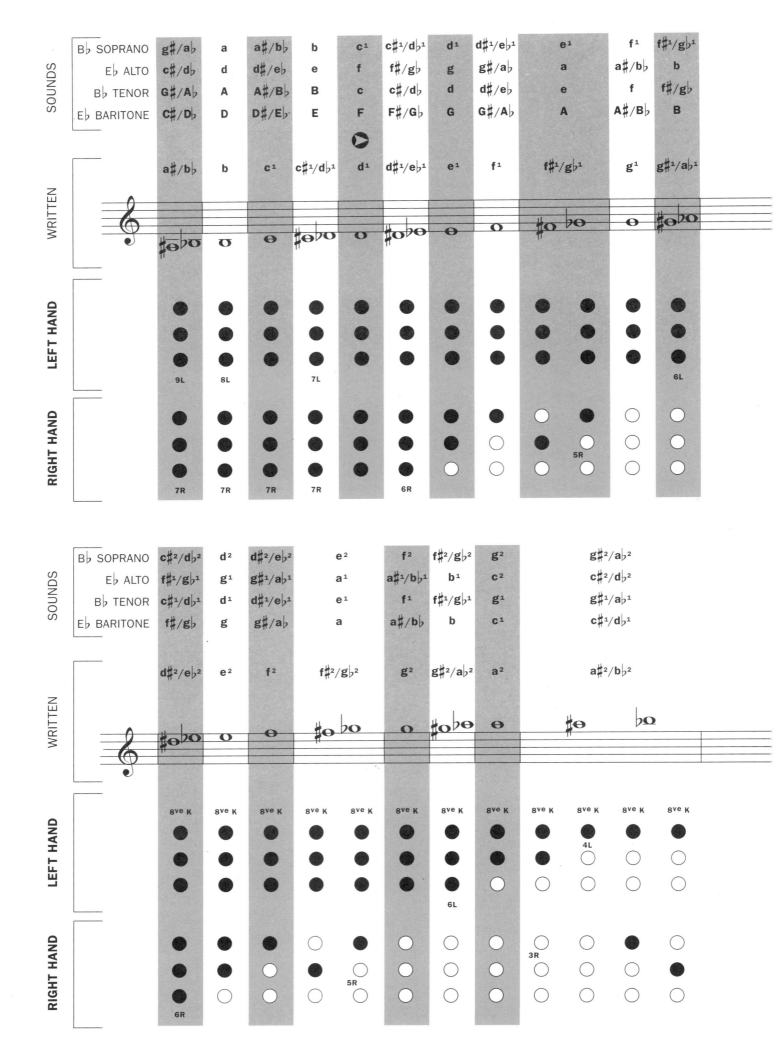

Indicates the lower limit of the best playing range

Saxophone Fingering Chart

g¹   g#¹/ab¹   a¹   a#¹/bb¹   b¹   c²
c¹   c#¹/db¹   d¹   d#¹/eb¹   e¹   f¹
g   g#/ab   a   a#/bb   b   c¹
c   c#/db   d   d#/eb   e   f

a¹   a#¹/bb¹   b¹   c²   c#²/db²   d²

Key labels (upper chart): 4L, 3R, 2R, 8ve K, 7L, 7R

a²   a#²/bb²   b²   c³   c#³/db³   d³   d#³/eb³
d²   d#²/eb²   e²   f²   f#²/gb²   g²   g#²/ab²
a¹   a#¹/bb¹   b¹   c²   c#²/db²   d²   d#²/eb²
d¹   d#¹/eb¹   e¹   f¹   f#¹/gb¹   g¹   g#¹/ab¹

b²   c³   c#³/db³   d³   d#³/eb³   e³   f³

Key labels (lower chart): 8ve K, 1L, 3L, 2L, 3L, 2L, 3L, 2L, 3L, 5L, 2R, 1R, 1R

Indicates the upper limit of the best playing range

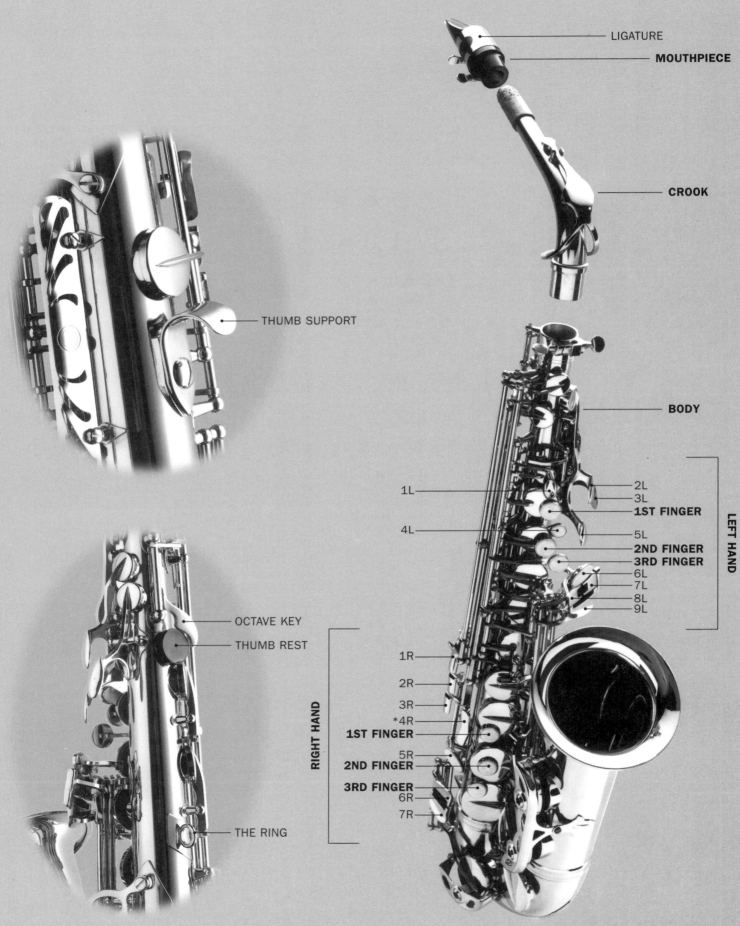

LIGATURE

MOUTHPIECE

CROOK

THUMB SUPPORT

BODY

OCTAVE KEY

THUMB REST

THE RING

1L
2L
3L
1ST FINGER
4L
5L
2ND FINGER
3RD FINGER
6L
7L
8L
9L

LEFT HAND

1R
2R
3R
*4R
1ST FINGER
5R
2ND FINGER
3RD FINGER
6R
7R

RIGHT HAND

* Not fitted on some saxophones

American Pie

Words & Music by Don McLean

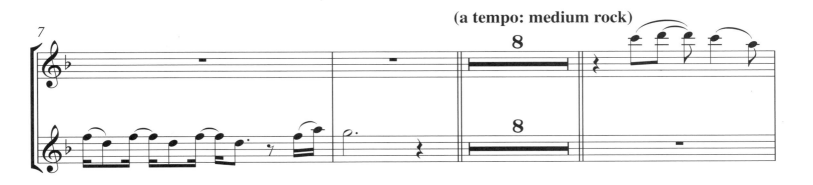

Angels

Words & Music by Robbie Williams & Guy Chambers

Baby One More Time

Words & Music by Max Martin

It Feels So Good

Words & Music by Sonique, Linus Burdick & Simon Belofsky

19

Livin' La Vida Loca

Words & Music by Desmond Child & Robi Rosa

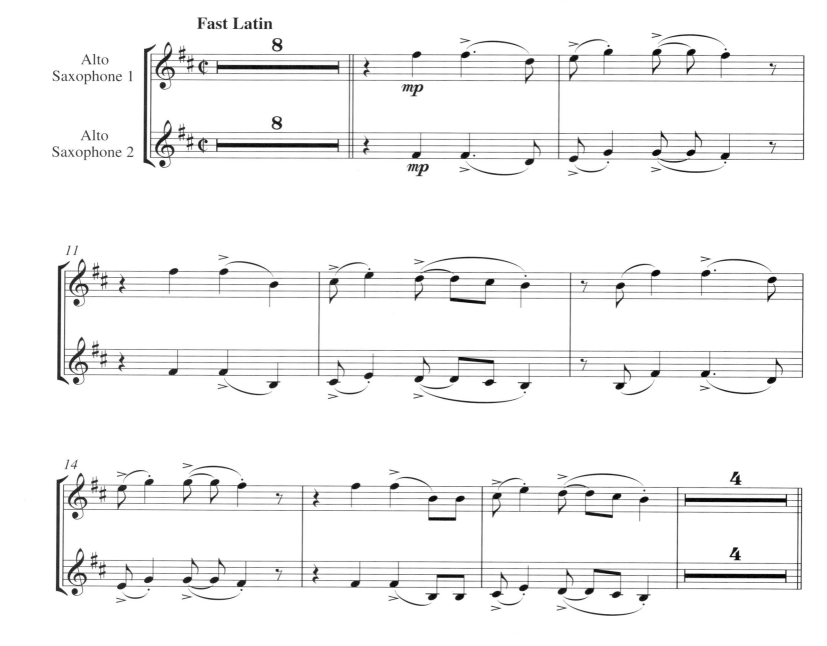

Man! I Feel Like A Woman!

Words & Music by Shania Twain & R.J. Lange

D. %al Coda

CODA

fall

31

Tragedy

Words & Music by Barry Gibb, Maurice Gibb & Robin Gibb

What Can I Do

Words & Music by Andrea Corr, Caroline Corr, Sharon Corr & Jim Corr

Play 4 times, gradually getting quieter

When You Say Nothing At All

Words & Music by Paul Overstreet & Don Schlitz

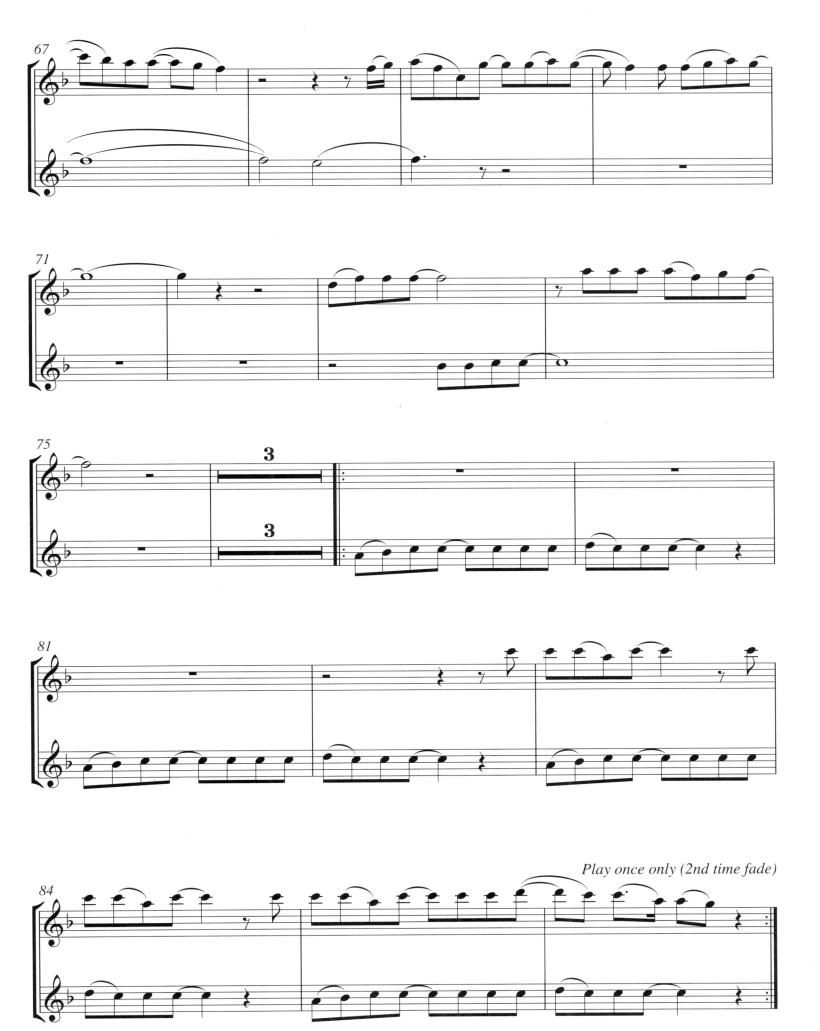

Play once only (2nd time fade)

43

When You're Gone

Words & Music by Bryan Adams & Eliot Kennedy